DOMINOES

The Swiss Family Robinson

LEVEL ONE   400 HEADWORDS

UNIVERSITY PRESS

Great Clarendon Street, Oxford, OX2 6DP, United Kingdom

Oxford University Press is a department of the University of Oxford.
It furthers the University's objective of excellence in research, scholarship,
and education by publishing worldwide. Oxford is a registered trade
mark of Oxford University Press in the UK and in certain other countries

This edition © Oxford University Press 2014

The moral rights of the author have been asserted

First published in Dominoes 2014

2027 2026 2025 2024 2023

17

ISBN: 978 0 19 424980 5   Book
ISBN: 978 0 19 463950 7   Book and Audio Pack

Printed and bound in Portugal by Gráfica Maiadouro

This book is printed on paper from certified and well-managed sources

ACKNOWLEDGEMENTS

The publisher would like to thank the following for kind permission to reproduce photographs:
Getty Images (Bettmann); OUP (Alamy); Shutterstock (Vibrant Image Studio).
Illustrations by: Peter Cottrill/The Bright Agency

DOMINOES

Series Editors: Bill Bowler and Sue Parminter

The Swiss Family Robinson

Johann David Wyss

Text adaptation by Alex Raynham

Illustrated by Peter Cottrill

Johann David Wyss (1743–1818) was born and lived in Berne, Switzerland. He loved nature, and often took his four sons for long walks in the Swiss countryside when they were young. He enjoyed reading the story *Robinson Crusoe*, and so he wrote a similar adventure story to read aloud to his children. The four boys in the book are based on his four sons. Years later, Johann David's son Johann Rudolf edited his father's 800 handwritten pages, and published the story for the first time in 1812 as *The Swiss Family Robinson*. The first English translation appeared two years later. Since then, it has remained popular with both children and adults. There have been several film and TV versions of the story.

OXFORD
UNIVERSITY PRESS

BEFORE READING

1 In *The Swiss Family Robinson*, a family lives on an island like the famous character Robinson Crusoe. Complete the sentences about them with the words in the box. Use a dictionary to help you.

barrel	cloth	rope	seeds	tools	wood

Mother, Father, Fritz, Hans, Ernst, and Franz on the island.

a Mother has some . . . .

b There's a . . . . under Father's foot.

c There are some . . . . in Fritz's hands.

d Hans has some . . . . over one arm.

e Ernst has got some . . . .

f Franz is looking at some . . . .

2 **What do you think? Answer these questions about the family's time on the island.**

a What do they eat?

b What things do they make?

c Where do they sleep?

Chapter 1 ○ The storm

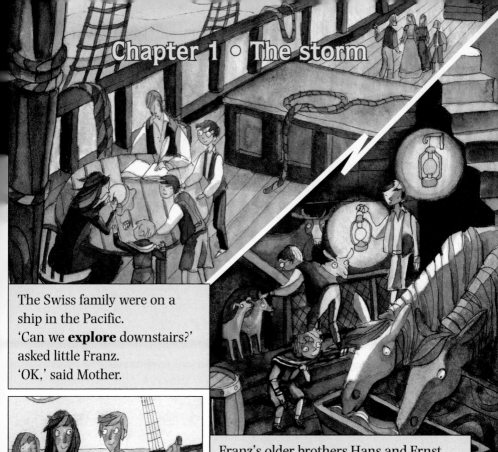

The Swiss family were on a ship in the Pacific.
'Can we **explore** downstairs?' asked little Franz.
'OK,' said Mother.

Franz's older brothers Hans and Ernst went with him. In the dark rooms under the **deck**, they saw dogs, horses, and a lot of boxes and **barrels**.

At the same time, their oldest brother, Fritz, spoke to some children on the deck. 'We're going to live in Australia,' said a Scottish girl, Jenny Montrose, excitedly.

Suddenly the sky went dark. Father stopped writing his **journal**. 'There's going to be a **storm**,' he told Fritz. 'Find your brothers and bring them to our room.'

explore to walk around a new place and learn about it

deck where you walk on a ship

barrel a tall round box; you put things to drink in it

journal a book where you write about what happens every day

storm a lot of rain and very bad weather

In bed that night, the Swiss family listened to the storm. Big **waves** hit the ship noisily.
'Are we going to be all right?' Ernst asked his father.
'I don't know,' Father answered.

Up on the deck, the ship's men were tired. They couldn't see in the rain.
'Oh, no! **Rocks**!' one of them cried. Just then, there was a **terrible** noise at the front of the ship.

Father ran to the deck. When he came back, his face was white.
'Everybody's getting into the ship's **boats**,' he said. 'Be quick!'

But when the family arrived on the deck, there was no boat for them.

wave a line of water that moves across the top of the sea

rock a very big stone

terrible very bad

boat a little ship

When they went to their room, Mother cried, 'The ship's going down. I can feel it!' 'I saw some barrels downstairs,' Fritz said. 'Let's make a **raft** with them. Then we can leave the ship on that.'

Father and the older boys went downstairs for the barrels. When Ernst opened a door to one room, two dogs ran out. Fritz and Father found barrels, **tools**, and **rope**, but they couldn't make the raft in the storm. So they waited for the morning.

Back in their room, Mother gave some bread to the boys. 'Are we all going to die tonight?' Father thought.

raft a little boat made from wood

tool this helps you to make or fix things

rope a very thick, strong string

3

The next morning, the weather was better. The Swiss family went up on the deck. The front of the ship was under the water, but they were near an **island**.

The older boys brought the barrels up from downstairs. Father brought some tools and made the barrels into a raft with ropes and **wood**.

That afternoon, the raft was ready. Father and the boys put it into the sea. Then the family took their things, and they got on it. But the waves were big and their raft was very little. Could it carry them all to the island?

island a country in the sea
wood the hard part of a tree

When they moved away from the ship, Franz said, 'Look! The dogs are in the water behind us.' Ernst quickly **pulled** them on to the raft. 'Rocks!' Father cried suddenly. 'Go left!' Big waves hit them, and water went over the raft. But slowly the island came nearer.

Mother was very happy when they arrived at the **beach**. The boys wanted to explore the **cliffs** and tall trees near them. 'OK,' said Father, 'but don't go far.'

After that, Mother began looking for wood. But just then, she heard Hans. He was in the water near some rocks. 'Ouch!' he cried. 'Something's got my leg!'

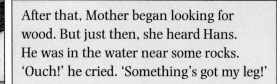

pull to move something quickly nearer you

beach the land next to the sea

cliff a wall of rock

READING CHECK

Choose the correct word to complete each sentence.

> beach leg boats raft rocks ~~ship~~ storm

a The family are on a ......*ship*...... in the Pacific.

b One night, there is a terrible ....

c Suddenly, they hit some ....

d People get into .... and leave the Swiss family behind.

e The next day, Father and the boys make a ....

f They arrive on a ...., and begin to explore.

g Something in the water has got Hans's ....

WORD WORK

The words don't match the pictures. Correct them.

a ~~tools~~

......*journal*......

b island

....

c boat

....

d cliff

....

e wave

f journal

....

....

GUESS WHAT

What happens in the next chapter? Tick the boxes.

a The first day on the island, Father makes . . .
   1 a boat. ☐
   2 a 'house' for the night. ☐

b Father and Fritz explore the island. They see . . .
   1 people from their ship. ☐
   2 nobody. ☐

c Fritz finds . . .
   1 someone from a different ship. ☐
   2 a nice little animal. ☐

d Father says, 'We must . . . '
   1 go back to the ship. ☐
   2 leave the island. ☐

e They take . . .
   1 animals from the ship. ☐
   2 meat from the island to the ship. ☐

f They see a dangerous animal when they are . . .
   1 on the raft. ☐
   2 under some trees. ☐

Mother ran to Hans. She put her hands under the water, and quickly pulled a big blue **lobster** off his leg.

'Here's our dinner!' she cried happily. After Mother **cooked** the lobster, the family ate it hungrily. They gave lobster and bread to the dogs, too. Franz thought of names for the two dogs. He called the white dog 'Bello', and the darker dog 'Juno'.

In the evening, Father put up ropes between three trees. He put **cloth** from the ship over them.
'Here's a **tent** for us,' he said.

Nobody slept much that night. They could hear the cries of different island animals in the dark!

lobster an animal with ten legs and two big claws that lives near rocks in the sea

cook to make hot things for people to eat

cloth you make clothes from this

tent a house made of cloth that you can take with you when you move

Next morning, Father said, 'We must find **food**, and look for people from the ship.' Father and Fritz left the beach for the forest. Juno and Bello ran after them. They found a river, and drank some water. Near the river, there were tall **coconut** trees, but how could they bring the coconuts down?

Suddenly, the **monkeys** in the trees began **throwing** coconuts at them!
'They're angry with us,' Fritz laughed. Then he and Father began hitting the trees, and the monkeys threw more coconuts down.

Just then, a little monkey **fell** from a tree.
'**Catch** it, Fritz!' Father cried.

food you eat this

coconut a hard white fruit with milk in it and a brown outside

monkey this animal with a long tail lives in trees

throw (*past* **threw**) to make something move quickly through the air with your hands

fall (*past* **fell**) to go down suddenly

catch (*past* **caught**) to take quickly in your hands

Fritz caught the little monkey. Then he and Father walked up a big hill. Fritz carried the monkey in his arms. 'Let's call him **Knips**,' he said. From the hill, they could see most of the island. They looked for boats or smoke, but saw nothing.
'So we're the only people from the ship here,' Father thought.

Then they found some fruit trees. 'Mmm. **Fruit**!' cried Fritz hungrily.
'Wait. Don't eat it,' said Father. 'Is it **safe**?'
'Father, Knips is eating it. So we can eat it, too, I think,' said Fritz.
Later, they caught two **birds** for dinner. After that, they walked home.

Knips /nɪps/

fruit you get this sweet thing from trees and can eat it; bananas and apples are different fruits

safe not bad or dangerous; in no danger of dying

bird an animal that can fly; you can eat some birds

'We're the only people on the island,' Father said that night. 'And we need more things from the ship.'

'Please don't go back,' Mother cried. 'It's **dangerous**.'

'We must,' he answered.

The next day, Father, Fritz, and Hans took the raft to the ship.

They found **seeds** and **guns**. And the animals were alive, too.

Father **tied** barrels to the animals. Then he tied ropes from these to the raft.

'Now they can swim easily behind us,' he said.

They moved slowly through the water. Then, suddenly, something dark went under the raft. It was a big **shark**! Fritz took a gun and stood up.

'Careful!' Father cried. 'Don't fall!'

dangerous able to kill you

seed flowers and trees come from these

gun a person can fight with this

tie to keep something in one place with rope

shark a big fish with teeth that eats smaller fish and sometimes people

11

READING CHECK

Correct eight more mistakes in the chapter summary.

Mother pulled a big ~~fish~~ *lobster* off Hans's leg, and she cooked it for dinner. Later that night, Father put wood between two trees, and made a tent for them. They slept very well that night because they could hear the cries of different island animals.

In the morning, Father and Fritz wanted to look for food and people from their plane. They found some trees, and monkeys threw apples at them. One monkey fell from the trees, and Father caught it. Later, they walked up a cliff and looked around, but they didn't see any people.

The next day, Father, Fritz, and Hans went back to the ship. They took animals from the ship, and tied them to boxes. Slowly they moved through the water on their raft, and the animals swam behind them. Suddenly, they saw something dark under the raft. It was a very big rock!

WORD WORK

1 Find six words from chapter 2 in the coconuts. Then use the words to complete the sentences.

a A ... lobster .... has ten legs, and it lives in the sea.

b You can make a tent with ropes and ....

c Help! Those .... are throwing coconuts at us.

d There are a lot of .... trees on the island.

e Look at that .... in the sky!

f Trees and flowers come from ....

2 **Find seven more new words in chapter 2 to match the definitions.**

a to make hot things for people to eat c o o k

b you can take this cloth house with you _ _ _ _

c you eat this _ _ _ _

d not safe _ _ _ _ _ _ _ _ _

e this big fish with teeth sometimes eats people _ _ _ _ _

f you can kill things from far away with this _ _ _

g to keep something in one place with a rope _ _ _

GUESS WHAT

What do you think happens in the next chapter? Read the sentences and write *Yes* or *No*.

a Dangerous island animals come near the family's tent. ....

b Father and Fritz find more people from the the ship. ....

c Father and the boys make a tree house. ....

d The family all work hard, and make a garden. ....

13

Chapter 3 · The tree house

The shark came nearer to the raft. At the last minute, Fritz **shot** it.
'Wow! You hit it, Fritz!' Hans cried.
After that, they watched the water carefully, but the shark didn't come back.

Mother met them on the beach. 'We've got a horse now,' Father said. 'More importantly – you're alive!' Mother answered.

That night, the family heard a noise, and looked out of the tent. Yellow eyes watched them in the dark.
'**Jackals**!' Ernst cried.
Hans saw a little jackal. 'It can be my **pet**,' he thought. So he caught it with a rope.
Just then, Bello and Juno **attacked**, and all of the bigger jackals ran away.

shoot (*past* **shot**) to use a gun

jackal a dangerous animal like a dog

pet an animal that lives with you

attack to start biting or hitting something or someone

'The island animals can easily attack our tent,' Father said next morning. 'We need a better house.' Some days later, they found some big trees on a hill.
Father threw a rope over a **branch**, and went up into the biggest tree.
'Here's our new house!' he said.

Father and the older boys put long **pieces** of wood between branches for the **floor**. Then they made the rooms. They put a big cloth over them.

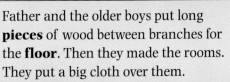

When the tree house was ready, Hans asked, 'What can we call it?' Fritz saw a **falcon** in the sky. 'How about Falconwood?' he said.

branch part of a tree

piece some, but not all, of something

floor the place in a room where you stand and walk

falcon a day bird that flies up in the sky and kills small animals by suddenly coming down on them

One day, Hans wanted to teach his pet jackal, Fangs, to **hunt**. So he and Fritz took it into the **forest**. Suddenly, they heard a terrible noise from the trees in front of them. Minutes later, hundreds of **buffaloes** began running out of the forest at them!

'Quick,' Fritz cried. 'Let's go behind those rocks!'

Hans took Fangs in his arms. Then the boys went behind the rocks.

Fritz caught a young buffalo with a rope when all the bigger buffaloes ran past them.

'Father's going to be very happy when we take this little buffalo home with us,' he said.

---

hunt to look for and kill animals   **forest** a place with lots of trees   **buffalo** a big animal like a cow

In the autumn, Mother made a garden with their seeds. The boys looked for food in the forest. They put it in barrels for the winter.

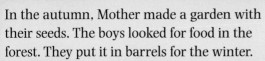

Father made a room for their animals under the tree house. Then he put his tools in the beach tent because there was no room for them in the house.

When the winter came, the family stayed in their tree house. And their animals stayed in their home at the foot of the tree. It rained for weeks. 'We haven't got much food,' Father wrote in his journal one day. 'Are our animals going to live? Are our seeds going to **grow**?'

grow (*past* **grew**) to get bigger

READING CHECK

Choose the correct words to complete the sentences.

a A shark attacks their boat, but Fritz *catches / shoots* it.

b *Hans / Franz* catches a baby jackal with a rope.

c They find some big *rocks / trees* on a hill, and make a house there.

d Hans and Fritz are walking *in the forest / on the beach* when they hear a terrible noise in front of them.

e In the autumn, Mother makes *clothes / a garden*.

f Father leaves *animals / tools* in their tent on the beach.

WORD WORK

1 Use the clues to complete the puzzle with new words from chapter 3. What is the mystery word in the blue squares?

a There are a lot of trees in a . . . .

b A . . . is a big animal. It can run fast.

c Hans has got a pet . . . .

d Father and the boys make a house in the . . . of a big tree.

e Seeds . . . into flowers and trees.

f Father and the boys often . . . birds for food.

	a	f	o	r	e	s	t	

Mystery word: . . . .

2 Complete the dialogues with these words from chapter 3.

attack   floor   ~~jackal~~   pet   pieces   shoot

Mother   Why did you catch a baby **a** .... jackal ...., Hans?
Hans   I wanted to have a **b** ....

Ernst   There are some big **c** .... of wood on the beach, father!
Father   Wonderful! We can make the **d** .... of the tree house with them.

Hans   That shark is going to **e** .... the boat!
Fritz   Give me the gun. I can **f** .... it.

GUESS WHAT

What happens in the next chapter? Tick three sentences.

a ☐ Knips finds something interesting.
b ☐ The boys catch a lot of fish.
c ☐ Mother leaves the island.
d ☐ Father and the boys make a new house.
e ☐ Hans gets into danger, but a pet helps him.
f ☐ Fritz shoots a very dangerous animal.
g ☐ The boys see a ship.

Chapter 4
The cave house

When they arrived, they couldn't see the ship any more, but they found pieces of wood by the sea. Their tent was in pieces – with Father's tools, cloth, and barrels all over the beach.

After winter, spring arrived. All their animals were alive, and little green **plants** grew in the garden. 'Very good!' Father said. 'And now let's go to the beach for my tools. I need them here.'

Knips ran after a little forest animal. He went into a **hole** in the cliffs. 'Where is he?' thought Ernst.

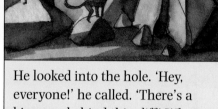

He looked into the hole. 'Hey, everyone!' he called. 'There's a big **cave** behind this cliff! What a good new home for us! Let's make a door into it.'

plant a small thing with leaves and sometimes with flowers

hole an opening in something that you can look through or go through

cave a big hole in the side of a cliff or hill

After hours of work, the door was ready. They went into the cave.
'You were right, Ernst, it is big!' Father said. 'This can be our winter house.'

For weeks after that, Father and the boys worked on the cave house. They made rooms, and cut windows in the rock.

One day, Mother found some tall plants in a **swamp** near the beach.
'With these **reeds** we can make a reed floor for the cave,' she said.

The next day, Hans wanted to cut more reeds. He went further into the swamp. Suddenly, he began **sinking** into the water there.
'Help!' he cried, but nobody heard him.

swamp a place with low wet land near the sea or a river

reed a tall thin plant that lives near or in water

sink (*past* **sank**) to go down in the water

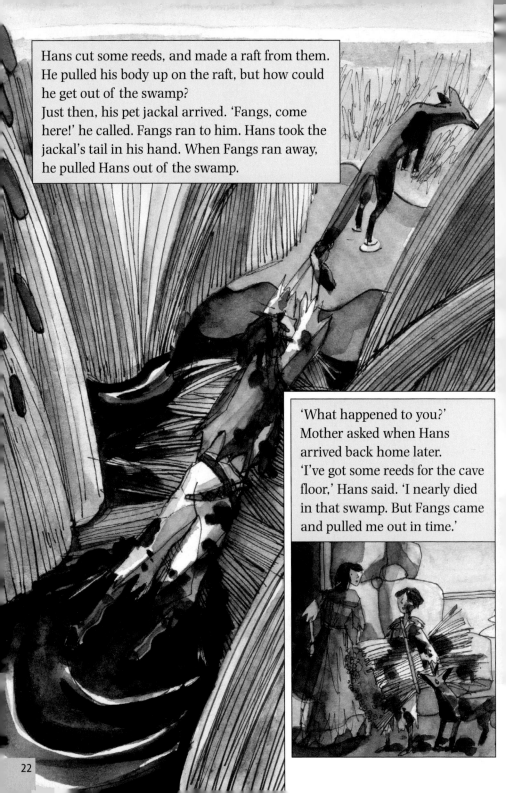

Hans cut some reeds, and made a raft from them.
He pulled his body up on the raft, but how could
he get out of the swamp?
Just then, his pet jackal arrived. 'Fangs, come
here!' he called. Fangs ran to him. Hans took the
jackal's tail in his hand. When Fangs ran away,
he pulled Hans out of the swamp.

'What happened to you?'
Mother asked when Hans
arrived back home later.
'I've got some reeds for the cave
floor,' Hans said. 'I nearly died
in that swamp. But Fangs came
and pulled me out in time.'

One hot day, the family were near the river. Their thirsty animals began drinking. Suddenly a very big **snake** came out of the water.
'Quick! Move the animals to the cave!' Father cried.

They stayed in the cave all day. Father and the boys stood at the windows with guns, but the snake didn't come. 'Perhaps it went away,' Father said that evening. 'I'm going to look.'
When he opened the door, their horse ran out into the swamp. Fritz went after it before Father could stop him.

snake a long animal with no legs

Fritz wanted to catch the horse. But the snake waited out in the swamp. And now it saw Fritz. It moved nearer.

READING CHECK

Are the sentences true or false? Tick the boxes.

		True	False
a	A lot of the animals died in the winter.	☐	☑
b	The tent on the beach is in pieces.	☐	☐
c	Fangs finds a cave in the cliffs.	☐	☐
d	Father and the boys cut a door into the cave.	☐	☐
e	Mother finds some reeds in a swamp.	☐	☐
f	Father pulls Hans out of the swamp.	☐	☐
g	They see a shark when they are near the river.	☐	☐
h	Their horse runs into the swamp.	☐	☐

WORD WORK

Find new words in chapter 4 to match the pictures.

a h o l e

b _ _ _ _ _

c _ _ _ _

d _ _ _ _ _

e _ _ _ _ _ _

f _ _ _ _

g _ _ _ _

GUESS WHAT

What happens in the next chapter? Tick two boxes to complete each sentence.

a Father . . .
1 ☐ finds some new fruit.
2 ☐ makes cloth from animal hair.
3 ☐ makes a boat with Fritz.

b Mother . . .
1 ☐ makes clothes for everyone.
2 ☐ thinks a lot about Fritz.
3 ☐ finds a new pet.

c Fritz . . .
1 ☐ explores the island in a boat.
2 ☐ can't come back to his family.
3 ☐ finds a message.

d Hans . . .
1 ☐ shoots an animal in the swamp.
2 ☐ goes swimming in the river.
3 ☐ comes home with a red face.

Chapter 5 ○ A message

Fritz heard Father and Hans behind him. 'Don't move!' they cried. Then he heard their guns, and when he looked down, the snake was dead at his feet.
'Hooray! We killed it!' Hans cried excitedly.

'This winter, we can be safe from storms and snakes in the cave house!' Father said. That autumn, the family made the cave ready for the winter months.

When the rains came, Father made some cloth from plants and animal hair. Mother made new **clothes** from this for everyone. One night, Mother said, 'Our island home hasn't got a name. What can we call it?'
'"New Switzerland"!' Ernst cried. 'And we're the Swiss Family Robinson Crusoes!' Everyone laughed at that, but they liked Ernst's name for the island.

clothes people wear these

Over many years, the family changed their garden into a little **farm**. They grew food on the farm, and had lots of animals – and lots of pets, too!

Little Franz was twelve now, and he liked to explore New Switzerland with his older brothers. They often went away for days.

'I **worry** about them,' Mother said.

'I worry sometimes, too,' Father answered, 'but they must learn to be men.'

'What happened to your face, Hans? It's all red!' Mother said when the boys came home one day.

'We found some **honey** in a tree,' Hans laughed, 'with lots of **bees**!'

---

farm a place in the country where people keep animals and grow plants

worry to be unhappy about something and to think about it all the time

honey this is sweet and good to eat; bees make it after visiting flowers

bee a little black and yellow animal that can fly and make honey

The next summer, Fritz made a new boat with Father. They made it from wood and animal **skins**.

When the boat was ready, Fritz wanted to take it out to sea, and to explore the island in it. 'All right,' Father told him.

When Fritz took his boat out across the **bay**, Mother and Father watched from the beach. 'Is he going to be OK?' Mother asked, 'Elizabeth, he's twenty-one,' Father answered. 'I was twenty-one when I met you – remember?' Mother smiled at that, but she didn't feel better about Fritz.

skin the outside of an animal's body
bay some sea with land in a half-circle round it

For many days, Fritz explored the island by boat. He swam in the sea, and he hunted in the forest. At night, he made a tent from cloth and branches on the beach. He slept in it.

One afternoon, Fritz caught lots of fish. Suddenly lots of birds came down from the sky, and they began to take all the fish from his boat.

Fritz caught one of these birds. Just then, he saw a piece of cloth on its leg. 'It's a **message**!' he thought excitedly. He quickly took the piece of cloth off the bird's leg, and opened it.

message you write this to someone

READING CHECK

Match the parts of the sentences.

a Father and Hans shoot . . .

b The next winter, they are safe from storms . . .

c Father makes cloth from . . .

d They call their island . . .

e Mother and Father . . .

f Father and Fritz make . . .

g Fritz leaves in his boat because . . .

1 plants and animal hair.

2 he wants to explore the island.

3 worry about the boys.

4 a snake in the swamp.

5 a new boat.

6 in the cave house.

7 'New Switzerland'.

WORD WORK

Write out the sentences with new words from chapter 5 in the correct form. Use the pictures to help you.

a Mother makes new

Mother makes new clothes.

b The family have a

....

....

c The boys find some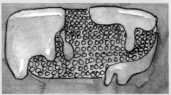

....

....

d Hans meets some angry

....

....

e Father and Fritz need animal

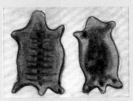

....
....

f Fritz goes across the

....
....

g He finds a

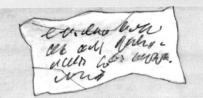

....
....

GUESS WHAT

How does the story finish? Tick one picture for each question.

a Who does Fritz find on a beach?

b What does the family hear?

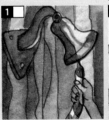
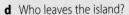

c Who do Fritz and Father meet?

d Who leaves the island?

Chapter 6 ○
To England

Fritz read the message.

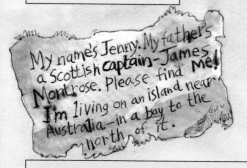

My name's Jenny. My father's a Scottish **captain**–James Montrose. Please find me! I'm living on an island near Australia–in a bay to the north of it.

He remembered the Scottish girl from the ship. 'Her name was Jenny. I must find her,' he thought.

Fritz looked for Jenny for two days. In the end, he found a sea cave, and he took his boat far into it. After some time, he came out of the cave into a little bay. There were tall cliffs all **around** it. He saw a girl in animal skins on the beach near these cliffs.
'Hey! You there!' he cried.

When the girl saw Fritz in his boat, she began running away. 'Wait!' he called. 'Jenny Montrose!' She stopped at this, and waited for him.

captain the most important person on a ship

around all the way round; to all the places

In Jenny's cave home, they talked about their last night on the ship . . .
'I got into a boat, but it sank near the cliffs,' Jenny said. 'So I swam into the cave, and found this bay.'

'We couldn't see it from our hills,' Fritz told Jenny.
'And I couldn't climb the cliffs,' Jenny answered. 'So I wrote messages.'
'But why did you run away from me?' Fritz asked her.
'**Pirates** came here last year,' Jenny said. 'I ran away from them. When I saw you, I thought, "More pirates are here!".'

pirate someone on a ship who takes things without asking

Jenny had some books with her. 'They're from the ship,' she said.

The next day, Ernst ran to the cave house. 'Fritz is coming. And there's somebody with him!' he told Mother and Father.

Fritz's brothers were excited when they met Jenny. They asked her lots of questions, and took her around the farm.

Father made a room for Jenny in the cave. She was happy. 'I've got a family again,' she thought.

When the winter came, the boys read books for the first time in years.

'Fritz's English is very good now,' Father said one day. 'Jenny's books are helping him.'

Mother laughed. 'It's not the books,' she said. 'It's Jenny.'

'This is an important day,' Father said one morning. 'We arrived on this island seven years ago – so no work today.' At once Jenny and the boys ran up the hill and shot their guns over their heads excitedly.

Suddenly, they heard the noise of a ship's gun. 'Somebody heard us, and they're answering!' Fritz said. 'Pirates!' Jenny cried. They ran to the cave house, but no pirates came.

The next morning, Father and Fritz took the boat out. When they left the bay, they suddenly saw a ship in front of them. They quickly moved their boat behind some rocks.

Then Fritz looked out from behind the rocks, and said, 'They aren't pirates. They're British!' So they went to the ship.

When they arrived, the captain met them.
'I'm James Montrose,' he told them.
'Captain Montrose!' Father cried. 'Your daughter Jenny's with us.'
'That's wonderful!' the captain said. 'I waited in Australia for her, but her ship never came. I looked for her for years, but found nothing. Then four months ago, we caught some pirates. They told us about a girl on this island.'

That afternoon, the captain visited the island. Jenny took him in her arms happily.

A week later, Fritz told Mother and Father, 'Jenny's leaving for England tomorrow. And I want to **marry** her, and go with her.' 'Then let's tell Captain Montrose,' Father said. And they did.

The next day, the captain married Jenny and Fritz. When they said goodbye to the family, Father gave a box to them. 'Open it later,' he said.

Jenny and Fritz stood on the ship, and looked back at their island home. Soon they could see it no more. Then they opened the box. In it, they found Father's journal: the story of 'The Swiss Family Robinson'!

marry to make someone your husband or wife; to make two people husband and wife

READING CHECK

Match the words with who says or writes them.

a My father's a Scottish captain.

b Hey, you there!

c Pirates came here last year.

d Fritz is coming, and there's somebody with him!

e Fritz's English is very good now.

f I waited for her in Australia, but her ship never came.

g Jenny's leaving for England tomorrow.

1 Ernst says this to Mother and Father. ☐
2 Captain Montrose says this to Father and Fritz. ☐
3 Fritz says this to Mother and Father. ☐
4 Jenny says this to Fritz. ☐
5 Jenny writes this in a message. ⓐ
6 Father says this to Mother. ☐
7 Fritz cries this when he sees Jenny. ☐

WORD WORK

Write new words from chapter 6 to match the pictures.

a around

b p _ _ _ _ _

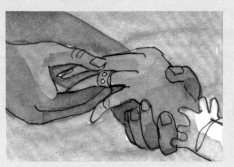

c m _ _ _ _

d c _ _ _ _ _ _

WHAT NEXT?

What happens after the story finishes? Tick some of these ideas, and write ideas of your own.

a Pirates attack Captain Montrose's ship. ☐

b Fritz and Jenny stay in England for some years, then come back to New Switzerland. ☐

c A lot of English people move to New Switzerland. ☐

d Falconwood is a big town in the end. ☐

e Mother and Father leave the island. ☐

f Franz is a famous ship's captain when he's older. ☐

g ....

h ....

Project A *Real-life survivors*

1 Read the text about a real-life survivor and complete the notes.

The real Robinson Crusoe

Robinson Crusoe is a character in a book by the British writer Daniel Defoe. Defoe knew about the story of a real-life island survivor, Alexander Selkirk, when he wrote it. Alexander Selkirk was a Scottish sailor. In September 1704, when he was 28 years old, a ship's captain left him on *Más a Tierra* Island, in the Pacific Ocean. Nobody lived on the island, but Selkirk soon learnt to survive there. He hunted animals for food, and he made clothes from their skins. He ate island plants and fruit, too. Selkirk built a little house, and he made tools from pieces of an old barrel.

Selkirk lived well on the island, but it wasn't easy to live alone. Once, he fell off a cliff, and he couldn't move for a day because there was nobody to help him. There was nobody to talk to, so he found animals and made them into pets. Selkirk stayed on the island for four years. In February 1709, some English pirates arrived there. They found Selkirk, and they took him home to Britain.

Name and nationality	Alexander Selkirk, from . Scotland .
Where?	an . . . . in the Pacific Ocean
When?	from . . . . to . . . .
What happened?	A . . . . left him on the island.
How did he survive?	He . . . . animals and ate . . . . and fruit, too. He made a . . . . , clothes, and tools.
What problem did he have?	It wasn't easy to be . . . . on the island.
How long did he survive?	. . . . years
What happened in the end?	English . . . . visited the island and found him.

2 **Read the notes about another survivor and complete the text.**

Name and nationality	Juliane Koepcke, from Peru.
Where?	The Amazon rainforest.
When?	December 1972
What happened?	Her plane broke into pieces in a storm. Juliane fell 3 kilometres to the forest.
How did she survive?	She ate a bag of sweets, and drank dirty river water. She followed a river and looked for a village.
What problems did she have?	She was hurt and alone in the rainforest. There were dangerous animals in the river.
How long did she survive?	10 days
What happened in the end?	She saw a canoe, and found an empty house.

The girl who fell from the sky

On 24th December 1971, Juliane Koepcke, from Peru, was in a **a)** .... plane .... over the Amazon rainforest. The plane flew into a terrible **b)** .... , and it broke into pieces. 17-year-old Juliane fell 3 kilometres to the **c)** .... below, but amazingly she didn't die! She was **d)** .... in the forest, and she was hurt. What's more, she didn't have any food with her – only a little bag of **e)** ....

Juliane needed to find a **f)** .... , so she walked along a river for ten days. There were **g)** .... animals in the river, and the water was **h)** .... , but she needed to drink it. On the tenth day, she saw a **i)** .... , and then she found an empty house. The next day, people visited the house and found her.

3 **Research these different real-life survivor stories. Choose one story. Write a text about it like the texts in activities 1 and 2.**

– Robertson family – on raft for **38 days**

– William LaFever – in desert for **3 weeks**

– Sophie the dog – on island for **4 months**

– Salamon Vides – in jungle for **32 years**

41

Project B *Newspaper interviews*

1 Look at the newspaper headline, and answer the questions.

Scottish captain finds daughter on island in Pacific

a Which tense do we often use for newspaper headlines?
Present Simple / Past Simple

b Which words are missing in the newspaper headline?
Nouns and verbs / Articles and possessive adjectives

2 Look at the sentences below and rewrite them to make newspaper headlines.

An English ship caught some pirates in the Pacific Ocean.

a English ship catches pirates in Pacific

A family from Switzerland spent ten years on an island after their ship sank.

b ....

The Swiss family changed an island into a small country.

c ....

The survivors from New Switzerland are going to arrive in London on Saturday.

d ....

The Swiss family's journal became a very famous book.

e ....

Jenny Montrose and her husband, Fritz, met the Queen of England.

f ....

3 Complete the interview with Captain Montrose with the reporter's questions.

> So how did you find it?   Was she alone?   Did it take long to find the survivors?
> Did you like the island?   How do you feel?   Did any islanders live there with them?
> Well, thank you for talking to us.   How did they get there?   Where did you find her?

Captain talks about finding survivors

When Captain Montrose arrived in London, a Daily News reporter spoke to him.

This is his interview.

Reporter: ..How do you feel?..........

Captain: Very happy. I looked for my daughter for years, and now she's with me again.

Reporter: ....

Captain: We found her on a little island in the Pacific.

Reporter: ....

Captain: No, she wasn't. She was with the Zermatts, a Swiss family.

Reporter: ....

Captain: They were on a ship to Australia, but it sank near the island.

Reporter: ....

Captain: No, they didn't. And the island wasn't on any maps.

Reporter: ....

Captain: Some months ago, we caught some pirates. They told me about a European girl
on an island, so we went there.

Reporter: ....

Captain: No, it didn't, because they found us. They heard our guns, and they came across
the bay in a boat.

Reporter: ....

Captain: Yes, I did. They call it New Switzerland, and it's beautiful.

Reporter: ....

4 Read the notes, then complete the newspaper interview with Jenny's words.

> **Jenny Montrose**
> - Sailing to Australia to meet her father when her ship hits rocks in a storm.
> - Gets into a boat but the boat sinks near cliffs. Swims to the island.
> - Lives in a cave near the beach. Eats fish and coconuts.
> - Writes messages and ties them to birds.
> - Fritz Zermatt catches a bird and finds her message. Later he finds her.
> - Jenny and Fritz marry on the island.

Survivor's story

The Daily News talks to Jenny Montrose.

Reporter: Why were you in the Pacific?

Jenny: ...I was on a ship to Australia.......

Reporter: Was your father on the boat with you?

Jenny: ....

Reporter: What happened to your ship?

Jenny: ....

Reporter: How did you get to the island?

Jenny: ....

Reporter: Where did you live on the island?

Jenny: ....

Reporter: What did you eat?

Jenny: ....

Reporter: You sent messages. How did you do that?

Jenny: ....

Reporter: So how did Fritz Zermatt find you?

Jenny: ....

Reporter: Now, you and Fritz did something important before you left the island – right?

Jenny: Yes. ....

Reporter: Wonderful! Well, thanks for talking to us.

5 A reporter visits New Switzerland and interviews the people there. Choose a different story character and write an interview with him or her.

GRAMMAR CHECK

Plural nouns

We usually add –s to nouns to make them plural.

birds, trees

When a noun ends in –o or –ch, we add –es.

buffalo - buffaloes, watch – watches

When a noun ends in consonant + y, we change the 'y' to 'i' and add –es.

country – countries

When a noun ends in –fe, it usually changes to –ves.

wife – wives

Some nouns have irregular plurals:

fish – fish, man – men, person – people

1 Write the plural form of these nouns. Use a dictionary if necessary.

a buffalo . buffaloes ....

b seed ....

c family ....

d child ....

e knife ....

f foot ....

g barrel ....

h monkey ....

i branch ....

j fish ....

k beach ....

2 Complete the sentences with the plural forms of the nouns in activity 1.

a There were a lot of young ...children... on the ship to Australia.

b We can put things in these old water ....

c They loved the yellow .... and blue sea around the island.

d No more .... from the ship came with them to the island.

e From the trees, ... threw coconuts at Father and Fritz.

f Hundreds of big .... ran through the forest.

g Father and the boys made a house in the .... of a tall tree.

h Mother took the .... and made a garden with them.

i Father and the boys caught .... in the sea for dinner.

j When Hans was in the swamp, he couldn't move his ....

k Father took guns and long .... from the ship.

GRAMMAR CHECK

> **Going to future: affirmative and negative**
>
> We use *going to* to talk about plans and make predictions about the future.
>
> We make the *going to* future with the correct form of the verb be + going to + the infinitive.
>
> *Father is going to be happy when we take the buffalo home.*
>
> *We aren't going to leave this island.*

3 Complete Father's words with the correct form of *going to*.

a The weather is changing. Winter is going to come (come) soon.

b Things .... (not be) easy in a tree house all winter.

c I .... (make) a room for the animals under the tree.

d The boys .... (find) vegetables for the winter.

e Mother .... (finish) the garden before the rain comes.

f We .... (not put) all our things in the tree house because there isn't room.

g We .... (not have) have much food. You can't hunt in the rain.

h I .... (leave) a lot of tools in the tent over the winter.

4 Complete the pages from Father's journal. Use the correct *going to* form of the verbs in brackets – affirmative or negative.

Thursday 15th

Winter is here. The rain isn't going to stop (stop) for weeks now. Mother and the boys .... (stay) in today because the weather is terrible, but I must go out. I .... (look) for some food because we haven't got much in our barrels. We .... (be) very hungry soon!
Some of the animals are ill. Maybe they .... (live) through the winter. Water is coming into our tree house, and we are cold all the time. Next year, we .... (make) a better house – we can't stay in the tree house next winter.

GRAMMAR

GRAMMAR CHECK

Imperatives

We use imperatives to tell people what to do or to give strong advice.

We make the affirmative imperative with the infinitive without *to*.

Be careful!

We make the negative imperative with don't + the infinitive without *to*.

Don't move!

5 Complete the sentences with the affirmative or negative imperative of the verbs in brackets.

a Find your brothers and ..... *bring* ..... (bring) them to our room.

b Quick. .... (catch) it!

c Wait! .... (eat) it! Is it safe?

d Please .... (go) back to the ship. It's dangerous.

e Careful – .... (fall)!

f Fangs, ... (come) here!

g .... (move), Fritz!

h My name's Jenny. Please .... (find) me!

i Hey, ... (wait)! Jenny Montrose!

j .... (open) it later.

6 Who says or writes the things in exercise 5? Write the letters.

1 Father and Hans tell Fritz this when they see a snake. ☐ g

2 Jenny writes this in a message. ☐

3 Father says this to Fritz when a monkey falls from a tree.

4 Mother says this to Father. ☐

5 Fritz says this when he sees Jenny on a beach. ☐

6 Father says this to Jenny and Fritz when he gives them a box. ☐

7 Hans says this to his pet when he's in the swamp. ☐

8 Father says this to Fritz when they find some fruit. ☐

9 Father says this to Fritz on the ship before the storm. ☐

10 Father says this to Fritz on the raft. ☐

GRAMMAR CHECK

Countable and uncountable nouns

Countable nouns have a plural form and uncountable nouns don't.

We use a/an with singular countable nouns. *Fritz saw a falcon.*

We use some, any, lots of, and a lot of with uncountable nouns and plural countable nouns. We usually use any in questions and negative sentences.

I found some honey. Did you find any bees?

We use much with uncountable nouns and many with plural countable nouns. We usually use much in questions and negative sentences. *I looked for Jenny for many years.*

7 Read the sentences. Are the underlined words countable or uncountable? Write C or U.

a The ship hit a big <u>rock</u> in the storm. .....C.....

b A lot of <u>water</u> came into the ship. ....

c There weren't many <u>boats</u>, and the Swiss family arrived late. ....

d They used some <u>barrels</u> to make a raft. ....

e They didn't have much <u>time</u>. They couldn't stay on the ship for long. ....

f That night, Father made a tent with some <u>cloth</u>. ....

8 Tick the correct sentences and rewrite the incorrect ones.

a There aren't some people on the island. ☐
...There aren't any people on the island.............................

b When you make a tree house, it's a lot of work. ☑
....

c We haven't got many food for the winter. ☐
....

d Mum's got some seeds, so we can make a garden. ☐
....

e We can grow lots of food next year. ☐
....

f Did you catch much birds when you went hunting? ☐
....

g The boys saw bees and found some honeys in a tree. ☐
....

GRAMMAR CHECK

Reference words

We use reference words when we don't want to repeat the same word again in a text.

Father ran upstairs. When he came back, his face was white.

They saw some barrels, made a raft with them, and left on that.

9 **Write reference words to complete the sentences.**

a Mother ran to Hans. ..... *She* ..... (Mother) pulled a lobster off .... (Hans's) leg.

b The boys gave food to the dogs, and .... (the boys) gave names to .... (the dogs), too.

c The island was beautiful. .... (The island) had forests, and .... (the forests) had lots of fruit trees in .... (the forests).

d A shark came near the raft, but Fritz took a gun. .... (Fritz) shot the shark, and .... (the shark) went away.

e Mother slept badly because the island animals made lots of noise. .... (Mother) could hear .... (the animals') cries all night.

0 **Complete the text with the reference words in the box.**

~~he~~	her	his
it	she	them
they	they	this

Little Franz is twelve now, and ...... *he* .... likes to explore New Switzerland with .... older brothers. .... often go away for days, but Mother always worries about ....

    'This island is big, and .... has dangerous animals on it, ... says to Father one day.

    'I worry when the boys go away, too,' Father tells .... New Switzerland isn't a safe country for children, but .... is their home now. .... must learn to live here.'

GRAMMAR CHECK

Sequencers and time adverbs

We use sequencing words like after, after that, at first, at the same time, before, then, later, and in the end to link story events.

At first, I saw some birds. Later, I caught a fish. Then I went home. After that, I cooked the fish. In the end, I ate it.

We use time adverbs like ago, at once, just then, now, soon, and suddenly, to talk about when something happened.

Suddenly, I heard a terrible noise. At once, Fangs was afraid. Just then, lots of buffaloes came. We soon caught one. This was hours ago. (ago = before now)

11 **Jenny is telling Fritz about her time on the island. Choose the correct words to complete her story.**

After / *Before* our ship hit the rocks, I went up to the deck and got into a boat *ago* / *at once*. Our boat slowly came nearer the island. *Then* / *At first* something terrible happened. *Later* / *Suddenly*, a big wave hit us, and everyone fell into the sea. I couldn't see any people in the water, but I was near a sea cave so I swam there. *Later* / *After*, I found this beach.

That was nine years *ago* / *later*, of course. The beach was my new home in those days. *Just then* / *At first*, I couldn't find any food, but I *soon* / *before* learnt to catch fish. *At once* / *At the same time*, I wrote messages and tied them to birds. *In the end* / *At once*, you read one of my messages and found me. *After that* / *Now* I'm very happy – I was alone for years, but I'm going to be with people again!

GRAMMAR

Going to **future, *yes* / *no* questions and short answers**

To make *yes* / *no* questions with *going to*, we use the auxiliary verb be + going to + the infinitive.   *Are our animals going to live?   Is Franz going to come with us?*

For short answers, we use the verb be.   *Yes, they are. / No, he isn't.*

2 **Captain Montrose's ship is going to leave New Switzerland tomorrow. Write the questions and answer them.**

a Jenny/go/to England?

.....Is Jenny going to go to England?.....

.....Yes, she is.....

b Captain Montrose/stay/on the island?

....

....

c Fritz and Father/talk/to Captain Montrose about Jenny?

....

....

d Ernst/leave/New Switzerland?

....

....

e Jenny and Fritz/marry?

....

....

f Father/give away/his journal?

....

....

DOMINOES Your Choice

Read *Dominoes* for pleasure, or to develop language skills. It's your choice.

Each *Domino* reader includes:
- a good story to enjoy
- integrated activities to develop reading skills and increase vocabulary
- task-based projects – perfect for CEFR portfolios
- contextualized grammar activities

Each *Domino* pack contains a reader, and an excitingly dramatized audio recording of the story

If you liked this *Domino*, read these:

Sherlock Holmes: The Top-Secret Plans
by Sir Arthur Conan Doyle

'This telegram is from my brother Mycroft,' said Holmes. 'He wants to speak to me at once about Mr Arthur Cadogan. Do you know this man, Watson?'
'I saw something about him in today's newspaper,' I answered.
When a young man dies on a London Underground line, top-secret plans for a new British submarine go missing. But who is Cadogan's killer, why did he die, and where are the missing papers? Sherlock Holmes and Doctor Watson must quickly help Mycroft to answer these important questions.

Journey to the West
Retold by Janet Hardy-Gould

'Tripitaka, can you go to the west for me – and for Buddha?'
When the holy woman Guanyin asks the young Chinese monk Tripitaka to bring some holy writings back from India, he says 'yes'. But how can he travel across rivers, and fight terrible monsters and demons, on his long journey? He needs three strong helpers – Monkey, Pigsy, and Sandy – to do that! But where do they come from? Do they always help? And can they bring the holy writings home again? Read this old Chinese story, and find out.

	CEFR	Cambridge Exams	IELTS	TOEFL iBT	TOEIC
Level 3	B1	PET	4.0	57-86	550
Level 2	A2–B1	KET-PET	3.0-4.0	–	390
Level 1	A1–A2	YLE Flyers/KET	3.0	–	225
Starter & Quick Starter	A1	YLE Movers	1.0–2.0	–	–

You can find details and a full list of books and teachers' resources on our website:
www.oup.com/elt/gradedreaders